David Mackay,
Brian Thompson
and Pamela Sch
wrote this book

Quentin Blake
did the pictures

Longman Group Limited
London Associated companies, branches and representatives throughout the world
© Schools Council Publications 1970
First published 1970
Second impression 1971   ISBN 0 582 19053 3
Printed in Great Britain by Hazell Watson and Viney

Schools Council Programme
in Linguistics and English Teaching

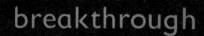

Doctors
and nurses

We play doctors and nurses
at school.

My friend is the doctor.
He's got a white coat.

2

Some girls dress up
as nurses.

I've got my doll at school.
She is ill.

She is very unhappy.
She cries a lot.

I have to take her
to the doctor.

Lots of children come
to see the doctor.
The nurse makes them
sit down.

7

One boy has hurt his knee.
He has to go to hospital.

This boy has spots
on his face.
He needs some medicine.

The doctor looks
at my doll next.

He gives her an injection.
He says
she mustn't go out to play.

11

I have to put my doll to bed
and look after her.

I give her some milk.

I sing her to sleep.
She will soon be better.

The doctor has made
everyone well again.

Miss Polly had a dolly
Who was sick, sick, sick.
And she phoned
for the doctor
To come quick, quick, quick.